VeggieTales®

New Testament
Bible
Storybook

With Scripture from the NIrV

This book belongs to:

_____

ZONDERk!dz

BIG IDEA®
bigidea.com

ZONDERVAN.com/
AUTHORTRACKER
follow your favorite authors

ZONDERKIDZ

The VeggieTales® New Testament Bible Storybook
Copyright © 2006 Big Idea Entertainment, LLC. VEGGIETALES®, character names, likenesses and other indicia are trademarks of and copyrighted by Big Idea Entertainment, LLC.

Requests for information should be addressed to:

Published by Zonderkidz
5300 Patterson Ave SW, Grand Rapids, Michigan 49530, U.S.A.

www.zonderkidz.com

ISBN 978-0-310-60448-8 (softcover)

Editor: Catherine DeVries
Art direction and design: Karen Poth and Ron Eddy
Production artist: Sarah Jongsma
Written by: Cindy Kenney with Karen Poth
Illustrated by: Casey Jones with Robert Vann

Printed in the United States of America

12 13 14 15 16 17 18 /WPW/ 20 19 18 17 16 15 14 13 12 11 10 9 8 7 6 5 4 3 2 1

Table of Contents

Unless otherwise specified below, all story titles are from VeggieTales videos of the same name.

1. Based on book of same title
2. From Are You My Neighbor?
3. From God Wants Me to Forgive Them!?!
4. From Are You My Neighbor?

Hi everybody!

Every year around Christmas, Bob and I and all our friends get together and put on a Christmas pageant at our church. Have you ever done that? Glueing glitter all over everything always helps to get me in the Christmas spirit!

Well, this year I decided to write a poem about the production—you know, document my experience. So here it is, "The Stable that Bob Built!"

Bob
designed
all the sets
for the
show!

This is the stable that Bob built.

This is the cow that mooed in the stable that Bob built.

These are the lambs, all cuddly and spry, that wandered off and followed the guy, who didn't know how to milk the cow that mooed in the stable that Bob built.

This is the shepherd,
who ate apple pie,
who cared for
the lambs, all
cuddly and spry,
that wandered off and
followed the guy, who didn't know how to
milk the cow that mooed in the stable that
Bob built.

Starring
Jimmy and
Jerry Gourd
as the cow!

It wasn't easy getting the cotton to stick onto the peas to make them look like sheep.

This is the angel who showed the way with a star to the three wise men who traveled so far. (It would have been easier if they'd had a car.)

She showed the way to the shepherd with pie, who cared for his lambs, all cuddly and spry, that wandered off and followed the guy, who didn't know how to milk the cow that mooed in the stable that Bob built.

This is the man, whom God designed, to love the woman so young and kind, that the angel told the shepherd to find.

She showed the way to the shepherd with pie, who cared for the lambs, all cuddly and spry, that wandered off and followed the guy, who didn't know how to milk the cow that mooed in the stable that Bob built.

Madame Blueberry made all the costumes. Aren't they great?

This is the baby, the Savior born, on that very first Christmas morn, the reason the star had shown the way for three wise men, who walked all day, to find the man, who God designed, to love the woman so young and kind, that the angel told the shepherd to find.

She showed the way to the shepherd with pie, who cared for the lambs, all cuddly and spry, that wandered off and followed the guy, who didn't know how to milk the cow that mooed in the stable that Bob built.

Larry played the part of a wise man... A very big stretch!

These are the Veggies who played the parts in the story that lives in all of our hearts, to share the news of the Savior born on that very first Christmas morn —all in the stable that Bob built! **End**

The Bible Story

I loved building the stable that the baby Jesus was born in for our pageant. But I didn't build the real stable. It's in Bethlehem. Here's the real story of how Jesus came into the world!

Jesus Is Born
selections from Luke 2:1-20

In those days, Caesar Augustus made a law. It required that a list be made of everyone in the whole Roman world. So Joseph went to Bethlehem, the town of David, because he belonged to the family line of David. He went there with Mary to be listed. Mary was engaged to him. She was expecting a baby. While [they] were there, the time came for the child to be born. She gave birth to her first baby. It was a boy. She wrapped him in large strips of cloth [and] placed him in a manger. There was no room for them in the inn.

There were shepherds living out in the fields nearby. An angel of the Lord appeared to them. And the glory of the Lord shone around them. They were terrified. But the angel said to them, "Do not be afraid. I bring you good news of great joy. It is for all the people. Today, in the town of David, a savior has been born to you. He is Christ the Lord. Here is how you will know I am telling you the truth. You will find a baby wrapped in strips of cloth and lying in a manger." Suddenly a large group of angels from heaven also appeared. They were praising God. They said, "May glory be given to God in the highest heaven! And may peace be given to those he is pleased with on earth!" Then the shepherds said to one another, "Let's go to Bethlehem. Let's see this thing that has happened, which the Lord has told us about." So they hurried off and found Mary and Joseph and the baby. The baby was lying in the manger.

He is Christ the Lord.

Well, that's my poem.

I sure hope you enjoyed my inside look at the VeggieTales Christmas pageant. We had a great time with the pageant this year! And Bob did such a great job on the sets. I mean, that stable is nicer than my house! I think I might just move into it until we need it for next year. We love sharing the message of Jesus' birth with everyone at our church. It's always such a great reminder of how...

God made you special and he loves you very much!

Today in the town of David a Savior has been born to you. He is Christ the Lord.

— Luke 2:11

Hey boys and girls!

I don't know about you, but sometimes I'm scared of more things than I care to think about! That's why I turn on my LarryBoy flashlight when I go to bed.

Last night, my flashlight went OUT! If I had knees, they'd have been knocking! That's when Bob reminded me of the very first story we ever told; it's the story called Where's God When I'm S-Scared?

Were those eyeballs in the closet?

"Junior! It's time for bed," Mom Asparagus said. "Besides, that *Tales from the Crisper* TV show is too scary for you."

"I'm not s-scared," Junior answered as he turned off the television and climbed the stairs.

Junior was sitting in the darkness of his bedroom when suddenly CRASH! A big, red monster appeared out of nowhere!

WHAM!

Junior's toy chest flew open and out popped ... a baby pickle?

Junior was happy to realize it was Bob the Tomato and Larry the Cucumber. "We heard you were scared, so we thought we'd help!"

Bob and Larry sang a song about how God is bigger than any monster!

"You don't have to be afraid, because God is the BIGGEST!" Bob explained.

There was something big and hairy casting shadows on the wall!

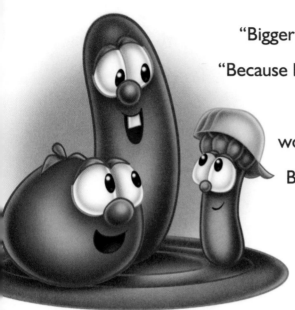

"Bigger than King Kong?" asked Junior. "Because King Kong's a really big monkey!"

"Next to God, King Kong would look like an itty bitty bug!" Bob said.

"Is he bigger than the Slime Monster?" Junior wondered. "Because he's the biggest monster of them all!"

God is bigger than the boogie man! He's bigger than Godzilla!

"Compared to God, the Slime Monster is like a teeny, little corn flake," Larry said. "Just look in the sky!"

"God made all those stars out of nothing," Larry explained as they looked out the window.

"Wow!" Junior said. "The Slime Monster can't do that!"

"And God made the animals and all the people, too!" Bob continued. "That's why we don't have to be afraid. Everything God made is very special to him."

"So God's the biggest of all, and he's on my team!" Junior shouted.

... and he's watching out for you and me!

Junior was beginning to feel like he could go to sleep until BANG!

"Yikes! It's Frankencelery!" Junior screamed. The monster that scared Junior on the TV show jumped right into his bedroom.

"My name is Phil Winkelstein and I'm an actor from Toledo. I just pretend to be Frankencelery on television."

Junior couldn't believe it. All the monsters that Junior was afraid of weren't monsters at all.

"Hey! What's all the racket?" Junior's dad asked, peeking in.

"Oh, I was just singing," Junior said. "God is bigger than any monster! He made the whole universe and he's taking good care of me, too!"

"That's right," his dad agreed. "It sounds like you're doing some good thinking. Now get some sleep. I love you, little mister."

"I love YOU, big mister!" said Junior. And then, in the dark, Junior fell fast asleep. **End**

I know whatever's gonna happen, that God can handle it!

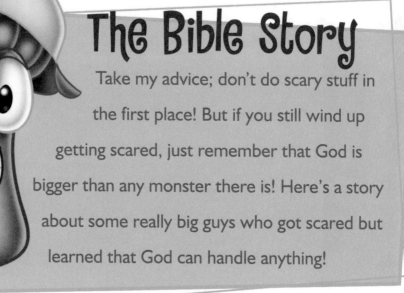

The Bible Story

Take my advice; don't do scary stuff in the first place! But if you still wind up getting scared, just remember that God is bigger than any monster there is! Here's a story about some really big guys who got scared but learned that God can handle anything!

Jesus Walks on Water
selections from Matthew 14:22-33

Right away Jesus made the disciples get into the boat. He had them go on ahead of him to the other side of the Sea of Galilee. Then he sent the crowd away. After he had sent them away, he went up on a mountainside by himself to pray. When evening came, he was there alone. The boat was already a long way from land. It was being pounded by the waves because the wind was blowing against it. Early in the morning, Jesus went out to the disciples. He walked on the lake. They saw him walking on the lake and were terrified. "It's a ghost!" they said. And they cried out in fear. Right away Jesus called out to them, "Be brave! It is I. Don't be afraid." "Lord, is it you?" Peter asked. "If it is, tell me to come to you on the water." "Come," Jesus said. So Peter got out of the boat. He walked on the water toward Jesus. But when Peter saw the

Right away Jesus called out to them, "Be brave! It is I. Don't be afraid."

wind, he was afraid. He began to sink. He cried out, "Lord! Save me!" Right away Jesus reached out his hand and caught him. "Your faith is so small!" he said. "Why did you doubt me?" When they climbed into the boat, the wind died down. Then those in the boat worshiped Jesus. They said, "You really are the Son of God!"

It's true.

We all get scared sometimes. But it's really important to remember just how much God loves us! After all, God made absolutely everything! And God is going to take care of all those things and all those people he created.

As for me, I don't even need my LarryBoy flashlight anymore.

I hope you'll remember how much you're loved the next time you're scared!

After all ...
God made you
special and he
loves you very much!

Hi there!

Today I saw two bikes crash. SMACK! Right into each other! It was a disaster. But what could I do?

First of all, I'm a busy guy. I have dance lessons and hairbrushes to find. There's my yodeling, my cebus, and my duckies! And don't forget that I'm a Pirate Who Doesn't Do Anything! So how can I possibly help them?

Junior had the answer. He remembered a very special story.

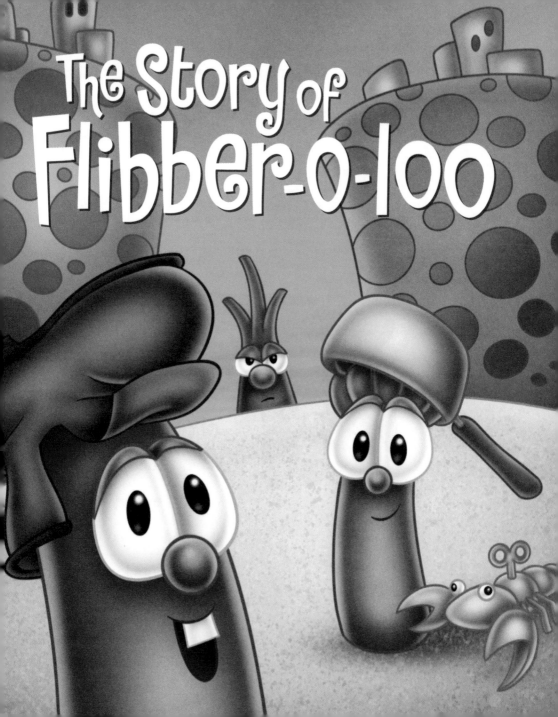

The town
to the west
thought IT
was best.

In a town to the west, called Flibber-o-loo, they thought they were best, cuz they wore a big shoe!

But those to the east in Jibber-de-lot disagreed with those folks, and instead, wore a pot! Till a shoe-headed boy and his blue plastic friend, went for a walk, down a slope, 'round a bend! And three shifty crooks jumped out from a rock —they knocked off his shoe, then they knocked off his sock!

But the thing they did next
was extremely un-funny: why
they shook him so hard that he
dropped his milk money!

But they didn't care—
they'd accomplished their
goal. So they put our friend
down—stuck his head in
a hole!

Things looked pretty grim
for our Flibbian buddy, his
head in a hole, his shoe
bent and muddy.

But then were these
footsteps? Oh, could it be true? Along
came the mayor of Flibber-o-loo!

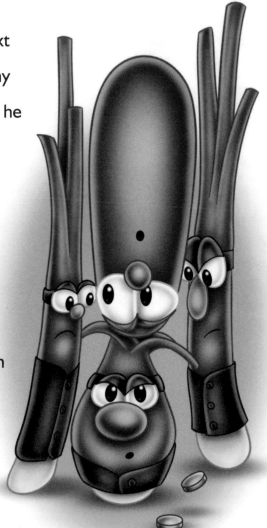

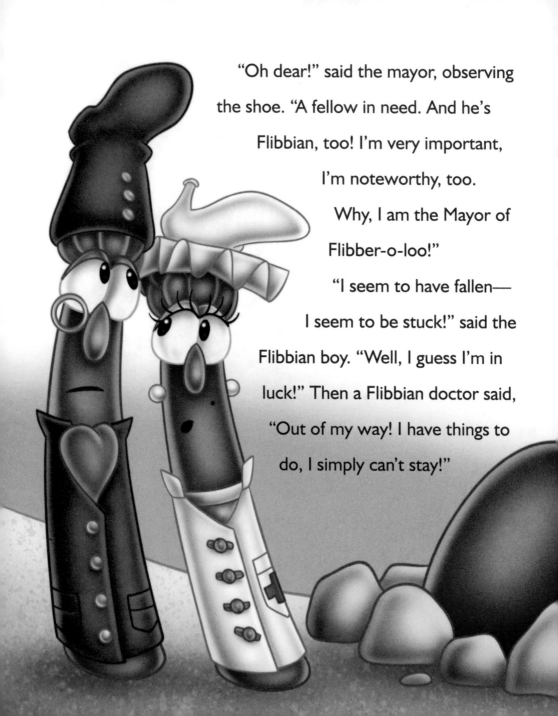

"Oh dear!" said the mayor, observing the shoe. "A fellow in need. And he's Flibbian, too! I'm very important, I'm noteworthy, too.
Why, I am the Mayor of Flibber-o-loo!"
"I seem to have fallen— I seem to be stuck!" said the Flibbian boy. "Well, I guess I'm in luck!" Then a Flibbian doctor said, "Out of my way! I have things to do, I simply can't stay!"

Oh! It was dreadful. How could they desert their Flibbian friend with his head in the dirt?

"That's it, then ... I'm finished. I'll die here, down under. If they would not help me, then who would?" he wondered.

Then the boy with the pot saw our friend with the shoe. "Oh, look!" he exclaimed. "He's from Flibber-o-loo!"

He looked at our friend, and he looked at the shoe. And then in his heart, he knew what to do.

We're busy! Busy! Shockingly busy!

God made us special and now I can see—
If you're special to him, then you're special to me!

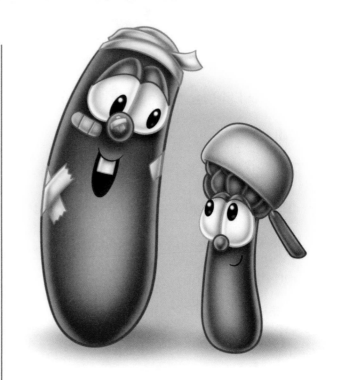

"He may be Flibbian, that's plain to see, but God made him special. Just like he made me!"

So he got him unstuck, and he picked up his shoe. And together, they walked back to Flibber-o-loo. They went to a doctor quite shocked by his pot. The Flibbian's friend was from Jibber-de-lot!

The boy with the pot paid the cucumber's bill. The Flibbians? They were touched by his goodwill! "If this little guy can take care of his brother, why can't we all try to help one another?"

So today if you visit the mountains of Flibble, you won't see a shoe or a pot. Instead they throw flowers and candy to nibble. I bet that you'd like it a lot! **End**

When you love your neighbor, loving means lending a hand!

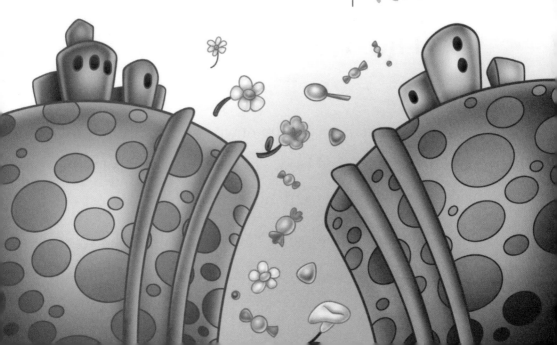

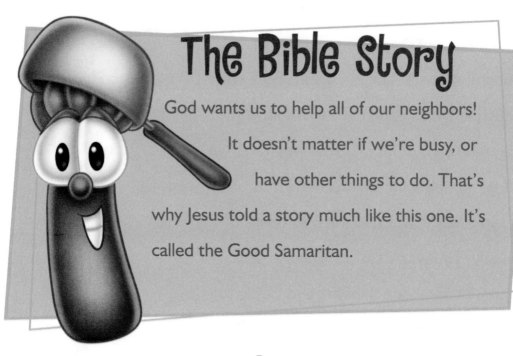

The Bible Story

God wants us to help all of our neighbors! It doesn't matter if we're busy, or have other things to do. That's why Jesus told a story much like this one. It's called the Good Samaritan.

The Good Samaritan
selections from Luke 10:30-37

Jesus [said], "A man was going down from Jerusalem to Jericho. Robbers attacked him. They stripped off his clothes and beat him. Then they went away, leaving him almost dead.

A priest happened to be going down that same road. When he saw the man, he passed by on the other side. A Levite also came by. When he saw the man, he passed by on the other side too. But a Samaritan came to the place where the man was. When he saw the man, he felt sorry for him. He went to him, poured olive oil and wine on his wounds and bandaged them. Then he put the man on his own donkey. He took him to an inn and took care of him. The next day he took out two silver coins. He gave them

> **When he saw the man, he felt sorry for him ... He took him to an inn and took care of him.**

to the owner of the inn. 'Take care of him,' he said. 'When I return, I will pay you back for any extra expense you may have.'

Which of the three do you think was a neighbor to the man who was attacked by robbers?" The authority on the law replied, "The one who felt sorry for him." Jesus told him, "Go and do as he did."

Thanks, Junior!

We all need to be reminded that God wants us to love our neighbors. We all have other stuff we want to do. But loving each other is the most important thing!

So Junior and I scrounged around and found some bike tires, a couple of wrenches, and even an unopened box of chocolate cookies! We're heading over to help those guys who had that big bike crash. We can love others by following God's lead because ...

God made you
special and he
loves you very much!

I give you a new command. Love one another. You must love one another, just as I have loved you.
— John 13:34

Hi everybody!

Just because I get a little grumpy listening to "What We Have Learned" after every show, Larry told me that I don't appreciate music!

He really hurt my feelings. Sure, he *said* he was sorry. And I'm just supposed to forgive and forget. Well, no way, bucko!

Now Larry wants me to hear a story. Well, being the reasonable tomato that I am, I'll oblige.

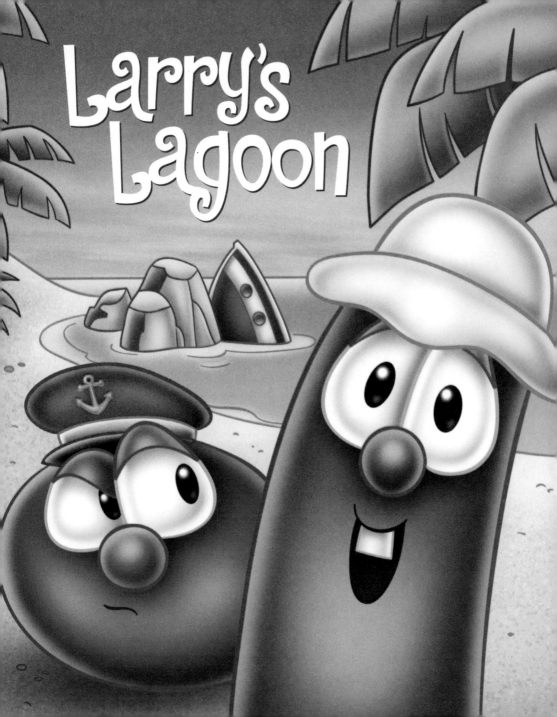

The brochure didn't say anything about this!

One summer Bob and Larry set sail on a three-hour tour with a millionaire, his wife, and a professor. Bob was the skipper and Larry was the first mate. But when Bob left the helm to check on their passengers, Larry crashed the boat right into a big rock!

The five castaways made it to shore, but now they were marooned on a deserted island. "You smashed our boat!" said Bob.

"Yes, what do you have to say for yourself?" asked Lovey, the millionaire's wife.

That night as they laid in their newly-constructed huts, Larry took a deep breath of the night air and said, "Gee, Bob, maybe this isn't so bad after all."

"Not bad? Larry, we're stuck on this island and we have no way to get home!"

"I said I was sorry," said Larry.

"Well, that's just not good enough!"

Larry was very sad. "He means I'M not good enough! I bet they'd be happier if I just left."

We most certainly had an accident. Someone has some explaining to do!

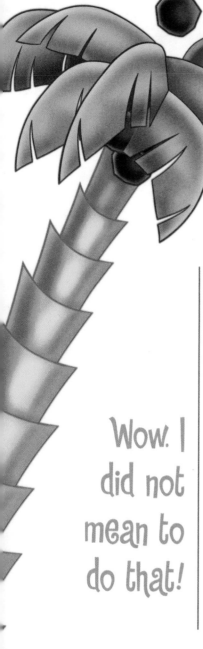

Wow. I did not mean to do that!

The next morning, the millionaire and Lovey saw the skipper up in a tree. "Has anyone seen Larry?" Bob asked. "When I woke up, he was gone!"

Suddenly the professor burst into the clearing with a giant bamboo catapult.

"If we wind it up and pull this cord, it will fling us back home!" he said, showing the castaways what he had made.

SpLo ING!! A coconut shot into the air, knocked Bob out of the tree, and they both crashed through the roof of the millionaire's hut!

"I'm sorry!" said the professor. "Can you ever forgive me?"

"It was an accident," the skipper said.
"I forgive you."

Then the skipper apologized to Lovey
and the millionaire, too.

"We know you didn't
mean to do it," said Lovey.

"We'll forgive you."

In love we can forgive. It is the only way to live!

"Boy, if I said I was sorry for doing something wrong and people still wouldn't forgive me, I'd feel terrible," he said.

Then they realized they hadn't forgiven Larry when he said he was sorry.

They ran down to the lagoon and found Larry floating away on a tiny raft.

"You guys don't like me anymore! So I'm just going to leave."

"But we d o like you!" said the millionaire.

"And we forgive you for smashing the boat!" added Lovey.

"Everybody makes mistakes," the skipper said. "We were wrong not to forgive you when you said you were sorry."

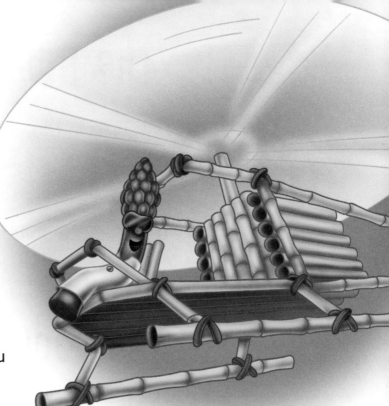

"o h! I forgive you guys!" said Larry.

WUBBA-WUBBA —it was the professor in a bamboo helicopter!

"Climb aboard!" said the professor.

Everyone was glad to be going home! They were also happy they had learned a great lesson about forgiveness, too.

Obey God and see that we can live in harmony!

The Bible Story

God sent Jesus to forgive us for our sins. And if God can forgive us, we should be able to forgive each other! Check out the story that Jesus told...

The Prodigal Son

selections from Luke 15:11-24

Jesus [said,] "There was a man who had two sons. The younger son [said,] 'Father, give me my share of the family property.' So the father divided his property [and money] between his two sons. The younger son packed up all he had [and] left for a country far away. There he wasted his money on wild living. He spent everything he had. Then the whole country ran low on food. So the son didn't have what he needed. He went to work for someone who sent him to the fields to feed the pigs. The son wanted to fill his stomach with the food the pigs were eating. But no one gave him anything. Then he began to think clearly again. He said, "Here I am dying from hunger! I will get up and go back to my father. I will say, 'Father, I have sinned against heaven. And I have sinned against you. I am no longer fit to be called your son. Make me like one of your hired workers.' "

He was lost. And now he is found.

"While the son was still a long way off, his father saw him. He was filled with tender love for his son. He ran to him. He threw his arms around him and kissed him. The son said to him, 'Father, I have sinned against heaven and against you. I am no longer fit to be called your son.' But the father said to his servants, 'Quick! Bring the best robe and put it on him. Put a ring on his finger and sandals on his feet. Let's have a big dinner and celebrate. This son of mine was dead. And now he is alive again. He was lost. And now he is found.' "

Larry! Where are you?

C'mon out! I forgive you! I really, really do!

You told me you were sorry and I should have forgiven you.
You're my best buddy! I do all sorts of things wrong, too. I'm sure
happy when I'm forgiven! And now, I hope you'll forgive me for
not forgiving you.

I sure am glad that God forgives all of us!

After all...
God made you special
and he loves you
very much!

Hey there!

I was shopping the other day, getting ready for Easter! I bought the biggest Easter basket I could find. And I got 182 multi-colored plastic eggs to fill with jellybeans and marshmallow chickens. And I got eight bags of green grass and four bags of purple!

I was very excited until Bob told me that maybe I wasn't paying attention to the real meaning of Easter.

He suggested I read a story called An Easter Carol. Let's see what it says!

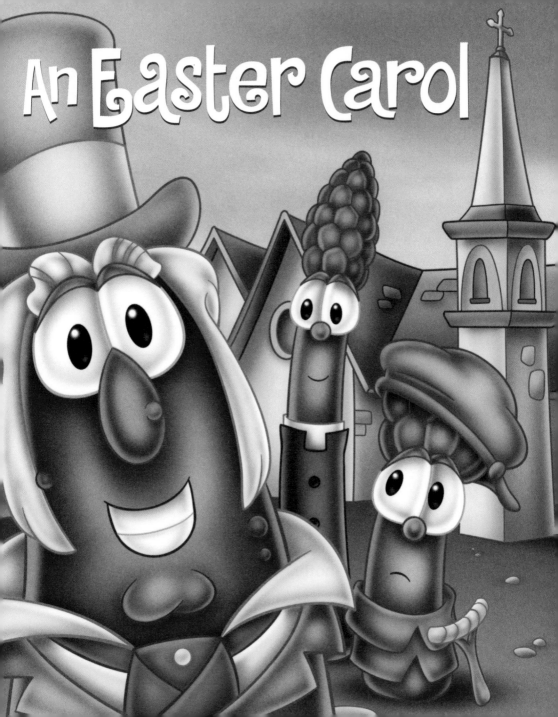

While Edmund and his dad prepared St. Bart's Church for Easter, Ebenezer Nezzer was hard at work making Easter eggs in his factory.

"Ah ... the satisfying fatigue of productivity!" Ebenezer chuckled.

Everyone begged Ebenezer to close the factory for Easter, but Ebenezer had another plan. He was going to destroy St. Bart's and build a place called Easter Land!

Bah! People should be buying more Easter eggs!

At midnight on Easter Eve, Ebenezer was fast asleep. WHACK!

Suddenly, he was awakened by a tiny angel named Hope.

Hope whisked him away and, before he knew what happened, Ebenezer was flying through the air towards St. Bart's Church.

Inside, he saw a little boy sitting next to his grandmother.

"That's you!" said Hope. "This is Easter past."

Before they left the church, Ebenezer saw the sunlight pouring through a stained-glass window that showed the birth of Jesus.

He just needs to find out what Easter is really all about.

A few minutes later, Ebenezer was watching himself as a grown up!

"This is Easter present," said Hope.

They saw little Edmund, who was very sick. "Mr. Nezzer isn't a bad man," Edmund told his father, "he just doesn't have something that we all have—the thing that lets us celebrate Easter all year long."

Ebenezer still didn't understand.

Back at St. Bart's Church, Hope tried
one more time to explain the true meaning
of Easter. She used the stained-glass
windows to show Ebenezer the
story of Jesus as she sang:
"A baby was born on a dark,
starry night. Some
followed the
star to see
the great
sight! The years
hurried by, and
the boy, now a
man, could make
the blind see with the
touch of his hand."

Death will never be the end, if you just believe!

"He hated injustice—he taught what was right. He said, 'I'm the Way and the Truth and the Light.'

"His friends soon believed that he was the one, the Savior, Messiah; in fact, God's own Son.

"But others, they doubted, they did not agree. So they took him, they tried him; he died on a tree.

"There is nothing to fear, nothing, heaven knows. He died for us to give us life, and to give us hope, he rose."

CRASH!

Hope's song came to a crashing end as the wrecking ball smashed through the first window of the church! Ebenezer woke from his sleep.

"Wait!" Ebenezer yelled as he ran down the street, through the door, and up the aisle of St. Bart's Church. "I was wrong! Easter isn't about plastic eggs. It's all about hope that this life isn't all there is!"

Edmund smiled up at Mr. Nezzer, who promised to use the money he saved for Easter Land to help make him well. End

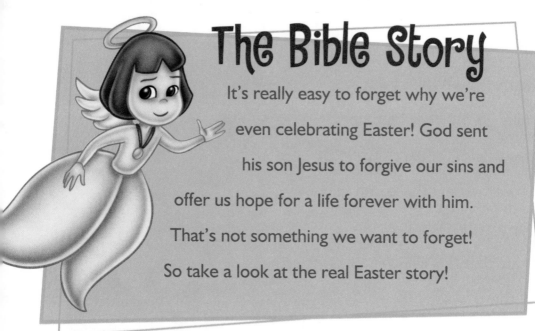

The Bible Story

It's really easy to forget why we're even celebrating Easter! God sent his son Jesus to forgive our sins and offer us hope for a life forever with him. That's not something we want to forget! So take a look at the real Easter story!

Jesus Is Risen

selections from Luke 24:1-10

It was very early in the morning on the first day of the week. The women took the spices they had prepared. Then they went to the tomb. They found the stone rolled away from it. When they entered the tomb, they did not find the body of the Lord Jesus. They were wondering about this. Suddenly two men in clothes as bright as lightning stood beside them. The women were terrified [and] bowed down with their faces to the ground. Then the men said to them, "Why do you look for the living among the dead? Jesus is not here! He has risen! Remember how he told you he would rise. It was while he was still with you in Galilee. He said, 'The Son of Man must be handed over to sinful people. He must be nailed to a cross. On the third day he will rise from the dead.'" Then the women remembered Jesus' words. They came back from the tomb. They told all these things to the Eleven and to all the others. Mary Magdalene, Joanna, Mary the mother of James, and the others with them were the ones who told the apostles.

> ## Why do you look for the living among the dead? Jesus is not here! He has risen!

Wow.

It's good to be reminded of what's really important. I mean, I like my yellow-and-pink-spotted malted milk balls, my fuzzy, yellow, squeaky chicks, and my white, furry Easter rabbit. But they don't mean near as much to me as Jesus! Jesus is what Easter is all about.

So, just remember, it's okay to enjoy the plastic eggs and baskets. I hope you remember the real reason we celebrate Easter every year, too. In fact, Easter is one of the reasons we know that ...

God made you special and he loves you very much!

God loved the world so much that he gave his one and only son. Anyone who believes in him will not die but will have eternal life. — John 3:16

Well, hello there!

Bob and I just bought new hats. Bob got a baseball cap, but I wanted something adventurous, like a fedora. Even the name sounds daring!

On our way home the Mushroom brothers knocked our hats right off our heads, and took them! As we were plotting our revenge, Princess Petunia saw us and encouraged us to read Minnesota Cuke. She said it might help us figure out what to do.

You'll never get away with this, Rattan!

Splat! Minnesota Cuke plunged into the powdery snowball as he grasped the golden carrot nose from the Indomitable Snowman of the North.

"Aha! Finders keepers!" shouted Professor Rattan as he snatched the treasure away. Rattan had ruined everything ... again.

LATER THAT DAY ...

"Rattan's just a bully, Minnesota," Marten said, trying to console Minnesota over the phone.

"I need to find Samson's hairbrush," Minnesota replied.

"Then I will have all

the power
and Rattan
can never bully
me again," he said
as he grabbed his
hat. "I'm going out
for ice cream!"
A LITTLE LATER ...

Minnesota smiled
at the beautiful
rhubarb at Malta Malts.
"Hello, Julia. I'm looking
for Samson's hairbrush."

"Don't, Minnesota. It's too dangerous,"
Julia pleaded.

But with a tip of his fedora and wink of
his eye, she gave him the address.

Minnesota Cuke, I always knew that someday you'd come walkin' through my door.

Minnesota Cuke headed deep into the catacombs and shined his flashlight on the cave drawings. "It's the story of Samson. Wow! What a guy!" Minnesota said, looking at the muscular Peach wrestling a lion.

He carefully crossed a rickety bridge that led to a pedestal holding the hairbrush.

"Congratulations, Mr. Cuke!" It was his archnemesis standing smugly at the other end of the bridge!

"Hand over the brush," Rattan ordered.

"Never! I have the power now!" Minnesota said.

But Rattan had captured Julia! "It's a simple trade, Minnesota. The brush for the beautiful girl!"

"Don't do it, Cuke!" Julia called.

Minnesota had no choice. He handed over the brush.

"We have to stop him! He's a bully! I've got to get even with him!" Minnesota shouted after Rattan disappeared.

Don't do it, Cuke!

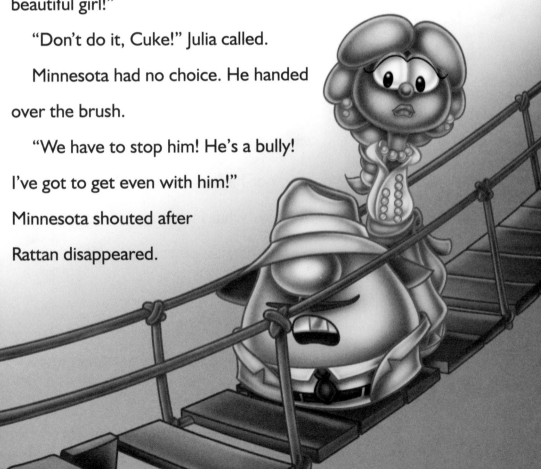

Stand back, all of you! I have a brush and I know how to use it!

"The Bible says we should love our enemies," Julia said. "We can't go around trying to get even all the time! That would leave the whole world in a mess!"

"I'm sorry, Julia," Minnesota said. "Being mean back to a bully just makes me a bully, too. But with that hairbrush, Rattan can rule the world!"

"The Bible says God gave Samson his power, not his hair or hairbrush," Julia said.

"I know what I have to do!" Minnesota said as he dashed off to catch up with Rattan.

MOMENTS LATER ...

"Stand back. I have a brush and I know how to use it!" Rattan ordered.

But Marten had called the police and

they arrived just in time for Rattan.

"Let him go, fellas!" Minnesota said. "God gives us the power to love everybody, even our enemies."

"No one has ever been kind to me before!" Rattan said. "I'm really sorry. Here's your hairbrush."

"Nah. You need it to cover that little bald spot you're getting," Minnesota replied as he fixed Rattan's hair.

"I think I'm gonna like being friends!" End

The Bible Story

Seeking revenge on our enemies isn't the answer. Look to God for strength and treat others with respect and kindness. Let's read what the Bible says about this ...

Wise Advice

selections from Romans 12:9-21

Love must be honest and true. Hate what is evil. Hold on to what is good. Love each other deeply. Honor others more than yourselves. Never let the fire in your heart go out. Keep it alive. Serve the Lord. When you hope, be joyful. When you suffer, be patient. When you pray, be faithful. Share with God's people who are in need. Welcome others into your homes. Bless those who hurt you. Bless them, and do not call down curses on them. Be joyful with those who are joyful. Be sad with those who are sad.

Agree with each other. Don't be proud. Be willing to be a friend of people who aren't considered important. Don't think that you are better than others. Don't pay back evil with evil. Be careful to do what everyone thinks is right. If possible, live in peace with everyone. Do that as much as you can.

My friends, don't try to get even. Leave room for God to show his anger. It is written, "I am the One who judges people. I will pay them back," (Deuteronomy 32:35) says the Lord. Do just the opposite. Scripture says, "If your enemies are hungry, give them food to eat. If they are thirsty, give them something to drink.

By doing those things, you will pile up burning coals on their heads." (Proverbs 25:21, 22) Don't let evil overcome you. Overcome evil by doing good.

> **If possible, live in peace with everyone. Do that as much as you can.**

Let's talk about this.

Bob and I have been rethinking our strategy. We've decided that getting revenge on the Mushroom brothers isn't such a good idea after all. We're trying to remember that God wants us to love everyone—even the Mushroom brothers!

So Bob and I have decided to go hat shopping again. This time we're going to pick out hats FOR the Mushroom brothers. Maybe they've never had new hats of their own! Doesn't matter. We know that it's better to do what's right by trying to be kind to them, even if they are bullies. That's what God wants us to do.

Because ...
God made you special and he loves you very much!

Hi there!

Have you ever played that game where you toss rings over a pop bottle and win prizes? Well, I am the VeggieTales champion! That's right. I always win! The other day we were at the carnival and Bob wanted this purple plastic squirrel. But I tossed my ring first and I won it! V-I-C-T-O-R-Y!

Bob said it was time for an attitude check. He made me read the story of Lyle the Kindly Viking.

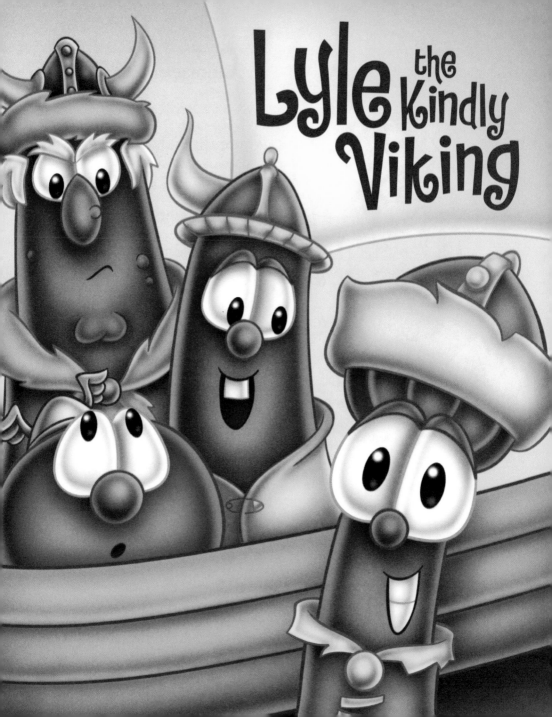

Once upon a time, there was a little village by the sea where there dwelt a band of Vikings. Just like other Vikings, they spent their days pillaging and plundering. Those are fancy words for taking other people's things. They were stealing. And their boats were so fast that no one could catch them so they could get away —every time.

But not all the Vikings were involved in this unfortunate practice. There was one Viking named Lyle who didn't like to go on the raids.

We never say please, or give stuff back!

In fact, when the other Vikings returned from their raids, Lyle would take the small bag of loot they gave him (along with some potholders that he made), and he would head out across the sea in his tiny boat.

When I share, I get my share of friends!

> I'm telling you, that boy doesn't fit the Viking style.

The other Vikings didn't know where Lyle was going. So, Sven and Ottar decided to follow him and see.

What they saw was troubling, to say the least. Lyle was taking his bag of loot and returning it to the monastery they had raided the night before. Sven and Ottar knew if Olaf—the biggest, meanest Viking—found out, Lyle would be in BIG trouble. So they decided not to tell.

Then one day, Olaf and the

other Vikings were out in their big, fast boat. "Hey, isn't that Lyle over there?" Olaf asked as he looked through his binoculars.

Sven and Ottar tried to distract Olaf so he wouldn't see what Lyle was doing, but it was too late. Olaf knew what Lyle was up to and got very mad. "That little Viking is in BIG trouble," he yelled.

Look, the monks saved Lyle. I guess if we had shared, there'd be somebody to save us, too.

It didn't take long for the Vikings to catch Lyle in his little boat. But just as they caught him, a huge storm blew up. The waves were so big that all the Vikings were thrown into the sea.

"Hang on, Lyle. Help is on the way!" the monks yelled as they scrambled to save Lyle from the angry waters.

"What about my friends?" Lyle asked when he reached dry land.

"Well, they were mean to us," the monks replied.

"I'm pretty sure God wants us to help everybody, not just those who are nice."

"Oh, all right," the monks said. "We're monks; we should know that."

So, not only did the monks save Lyle, they saved all the Vikings that day—all because Lyle had made friends with them by sharing.

The Bible Story

Putting others first isn't always easy. Just remember that God loves you. He sent his Son Jesus who was willing to put all of us first. You can read in the Bible about how God wants us to be cheerful givers—to everyone.

A Cheerful Giver

selections from 2 Corinthians 9:7-9, 11-15

You should each give what you have decided in your heart to give. You shouldn't give if you don't want to. You shouldn't give because you are forced to. God loves a cheerful giver. And God is able to shower all kinds of blessings on you. In all things and at all times you will have everything you need. You will do more and more good works. It is written, "They have spread their

gifts around to poor people. Their good works continue forever."
(Psalm 112:9) You will be made rich in every way. Then you can
always give freely. We will take your many gifts to the people
who need them. And they will give thanks to God. Your gifts
meet the needs of God's people. And that's not all. Your gifts also
cause many people to thank God. You have shown yourselves to

be worthy by what you have
given. So people will praise God
because you obey him. That
proves that you really believe
the good news about Christ.
They will also praise God
because you share freely with
them and with everyone else.

> They will also praise God because you share freely with them and with everyone else.

Their hearts will be filled with longing for you when they pray for
you. God has given you grace that is better than anything.

Let us give thanks to God for his gift. It is so great that no one
can tell how wonderful it really is!

Attitude checked.

I really do like that plastic squirrel. And even more than the plastic squirrel, I liked winning. But I like Bob more than either of those things. So I gave the squirrel to Bob.

It's important to treat others fairly and to be kind, like Lyle. And you know what? It's really fun to share!

It's time for me to start putting others first, no matter what I'm doing. That way, everyone wins!

I hope you'll remember that God wants you to put others first, too.

After all ...
God made you special and he loves you very much!

None of you should look out just for your own good. You should also look out for the good of others.

— Philippians 2:4

Hi, boys and girls!

Have you ever seen someone and thought, "Wow! They sure are different!" I have. In fact, there's this kid in my home economics class who likes to wear his oven mit on his head. The kids and I decided he was a little, um ... crazy!

After class, I bumped into Junior Asparagus and told him all about him. He told me to read a story about some gourds that were really different, too. I love stories ... so why not!

WHOOSH

went the elevator on the U.S.S. Applepies as Captain Bob stepped out on the control deck.

"Ah, Cap'n Bob!" said Scooter, the spaceship's engineer. "We've only five minutes till that popcorn meteor smashes us to bits!"

Everyone gasped. They were in big trouble.

"Is it caramel or cheese?" asked Larry. "That cheese stuff gets stuck to my tooth."

"Hey, maybe they can help!" Junior said, pointing to the gourds working by themselves.

"They're the 'new guys!' " Scooter said.

The ship
has no
power!
She's dead
in the
water!
She's stuck!

"All they do is eat and sing. I think they're a wee bit crazy!"

"I'm Junior, and we've got a problem," he said to the new guys.

"I'm Jimmy."

"I'm Jerry. We're the new guys."

"I heard," Junior said. "Why do you guys sing and eat all the time?"

"Why don't you?" asked Jerry.

"I dunno!" said Junior. "Because it's weird ... uh, I mean different."

A popcorn ball meteor. The worst kind!

We're hungry. It's our metabolism.

"Sometimes differences can be good," said Jimmy Gourd. "In fact, I think I could eat a whole bus!"

"I think I could eat a whole spaceship!" said Jerry.

"I could eat a whole planet!" said Jimmy.

"A whole planet?" Junior had an idea.

"How would you like to help

save the ship?"

"Gosh," said Jimmy,

that'd be swell!"

So Bob, Larry,

Junior, and Scooter

helped the Gourds

into the only two

escape pods on the

ship.

"We've only got two

minutes left!" said Bob.

"I sure hope this works!"

The pods fired up and shot deep

into space until PLOMPH!!! The pods hit

the meteor!

We're all
pretty
different.
Some are
skinny, some
are stout,

"Let's eat it!" the gourds shouted. And they ate and ate and ate and ATE!

Meanwhile, back on the ship, everyone was very nervous.

"Only ten seconds left!" said Bob. "I sure hope they were hungry! Five ... Four ... Three ... Two ... ONE!!!"

THUNK! Jimmy and Jerry knocked on the door!

"Boy, am I full!" said Jimmy.

"Mission accomplished. You saved the ship!" said Bob.

"Aw ... It was nothing!"

"Nothing?" said Scooter. "You consumed fourteen thousand metric tons o' popcorn, lads!"

"Well," said Jimmy, "maybe it's a little something."

"To think I wouldn't be your friend just because you guys are different!" said Scooter. "I'm glad you're my friends!"

"We are, too!" agreed very full and happy Jimmy and Jerry. **End**

but the inside is the part that we're supposed to care about!

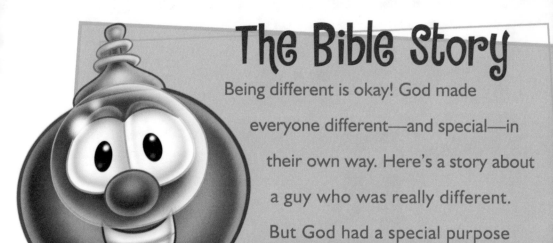

The Bible Story

Being different is okay! God made everyone different—and special—in their own way. Here's a story about a guy who was really different. But God had a special purpose for him, too.

The Conversion of Paul
selections from Acts 9:1-19

Saul continued to oppose the Lord's followers. On his journey, suddenly a light from heaven flashed around him. He fell to the ground. He heard a voice speak to him.

"Saul! Saul!" the voice said. "Why are you opposing me?"

"Who are you, Lord?" Saul asked.

"I am Jesus," he replied. "I am the one you are opposing. Now get up and go into the city. There you will be told what to do."

The men traveling with Saul stood there. They weren't able to speak. They had heard the sound. But they didn't see anyone. Saul got up from the ground. He opened his eyes, but he couldn't see. So they led him by the hand into [the city]. For three days he was blind. He didn't eat or drink anything.

In [the city] there was a believer named Ananias. The Lord called out to him in a vision. "Go to the house of Judas. Ask for a man named Saul. He is praying. "Go! I have chosen this man to work for me. He will carry my name to those who aren't Jews and to their kings. He will bring my name to the people of Israel."

Ananias went to the house. He placed his hands on Saul [and said,] "Brother Saul, you saw the Lord Jesus on the road as you were coming here. He has sent me so that you will be able to see again. You will be filled with the Holy Spirit."

Something like scales fell from Saul's eyes.

Something like scales fell from Saul's eyes. And he could see again. He got up and was baptized.

Back to school!

I went back to my home economics class and decided to clear up my differences with the new kid! I went over and introduced myself, and I discovered he was a lot of fun! He taught me a really great recipe for toast, and we had a great time. I also discovered that it's kind of fun to wear an oven mit on my head. After all, I don't have any hands to put it on!

Isn't it wonderful that God made everyone different? It sure does make things interesting—and a lot more fun, too!

Remember ...
God made you special and he loves you very much!

Christ has accepted you. So accept one another in order to bring praise to God.
— Romans 15:17

Hello boys and girls!

I have a new hobby. Gardening! Nothing lifts the spirits like a little dabbling in the horticultural arts. And I'm really good at it, too. I'm going to enter my dandelion patch in the Lawn and Garden show. My neighbor, Mrs. Stephenson, is entering the contest, too. But Percy Pea told me that she has poison ivy in her flower bed.

I was just on my way to tell the judges about that when Bob stopped me. He said he had a story I'd better listen to before I tell anybody what I'd heard.

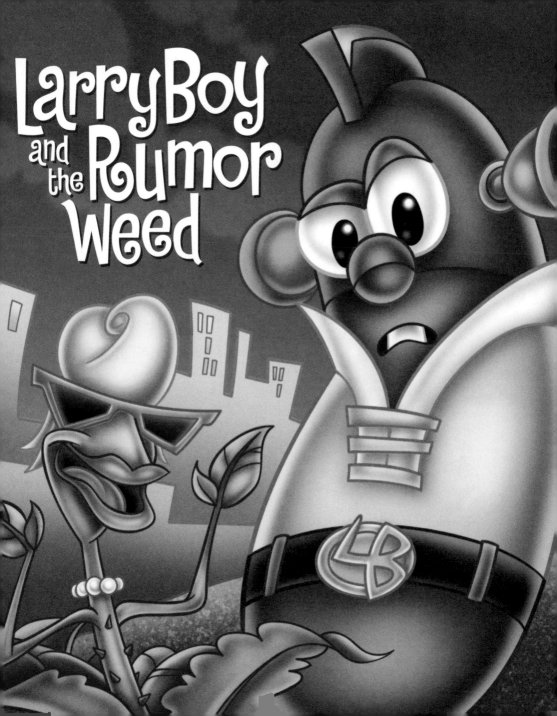

"Thank you so much for having me!" Alfred the butler said as he finished his Career Day speech at the Veggie Valley Grade School. "I'd love to stay longer but I'm very tired. I'd better go home and 'recharge my batteries!'"

LATER THAT DAY ...

"Did you hear what Mr. Alfred said?" Junior asked Laura as they walked home from school.

"Yeah," Laura replied, "he said he had to go home and recharge his batteries. I think Mr. Alfred IS ... A ... ROBOT."

Suddenly a strange voice came out of nowhere. "What was that you said?"

"Who said that?" Laura asked as she looked down and saw ... a TALKING WEED.

"C'mon, tell me what it is you're keeping to yourselves," the weed continued. "Didn't your parents ever teach you to share?"

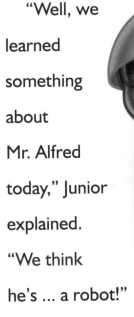

"Well, we learned something about Mr. Alfred today," Junior explained. "We think he's ... a robot!"

I'm a talking weed. You're a talking carrot. Your point was?

I'm a
Rumor Weed!
A tiny little
story is all
I need.

MOMENTS LATER ...

The weed showed up in Percy Pea's yard. She told Percy that Mr. Alfred was a dangerous robot. Soon, the Rumor Weed was introducing herself all over Bumblyburg.

"So what is a rumor?" Mr. Nezzer asked.

"A rumor starts with a story," the weed explained. "Maybe it's true, maybe not. But once you repeat it, it's hard to defeat it. Now look at the mess that you've got!"

It was true, every time someone in the city repeated the rumor, the weed got bigger. Soon, weeds were popping up all over the city. They were feeding on the story that Junior and Laura had started.

The weed was growing powerful roots capable of breaking sidewalks and even going through walls. If something wasn't done about this terrible Rumor Weed, the city would be ruined!

There was only one thing to do. The mayor picked up the phone and called ... LarryBoy!

I am that hero!

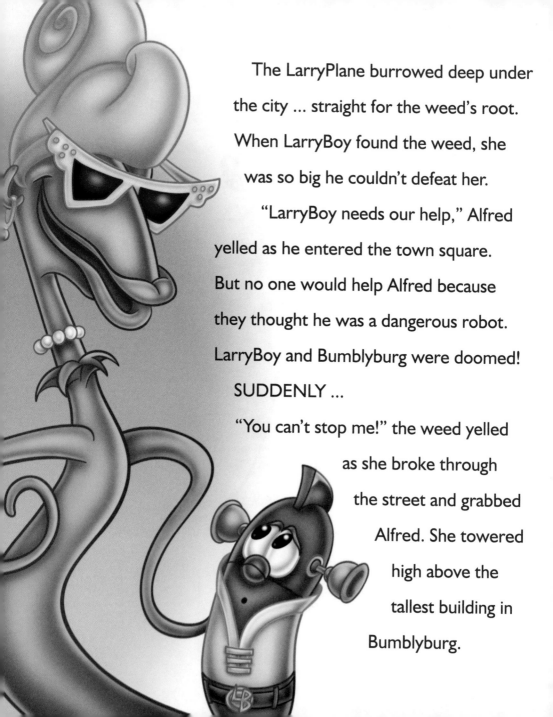

The LarryPlane burrowed deep under the city ... straight for the weed's root. When LarryBoy found the weed, she was so big he couldn't defeat her.

"LarryBoy needs our help," Alfred yelled as he entered the town square. But no one would help Alfred because they thought he was a dangerous robot. LarryBoy and Bumblyburg were doomed! SUDDENLY ...

"You can't stop me!" the weed yelled as she broke through the street and grabbed Alfred. She towered high above the tallest building in Bumblyburg.

MEANWHILE ...

On the street, Junior's dad asked the kids what happened.

"Well, we heard Mr. Alfred say that he needed to recharge his batteries," Laura explained. "We thought he was a robot."

"Mr. Alfred isn't a robot," Dad Asparagus said. "He's a very nice man."

As he said those nice words, the weed sprouted blooms.

Soon, the whole town began saying nice words about Alfred, and the Rumor Weed turned into a beautiful flower.

"God doesn't want us to spread words that hurt, he wants us to spread nice words." End

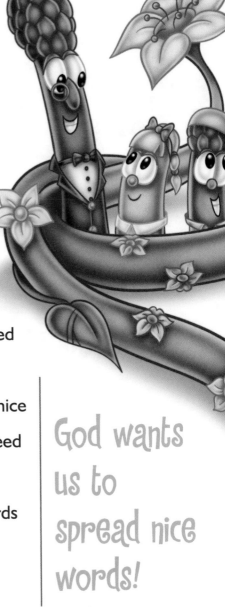

God wants us to spread nice words!

The Bible Story

The Rumor Weed is much more dangerous than a real weed in the garden. I couldn't even defeat it by attacking the roots! The only way to beat the Rumor Weed was by spreading nice words. Here's a great Bible passage about this ...

New Life ... New Ways
selections from Colossians 3:8-17

But now here are the kinds of things you must get rid of. You must put away anger, rage, hate and lies. Let no dirty words come out of your mouths. Don't lie to each other. You have gotten rid of your old way of life and its habits. You have started living a new life. It is being made new so that what you know has the

Creator's likeness … There is no slave or free person. But Christ is everything. And he is in everything.

You are God's chosen people. You are holy and dearly loved. So put on tender mercy and kindness as if they were your clothes. Don't be proud. Be gentle and patient. Put up with each other. Forgive the things you are holding against one another. Forgive, just as the Lord forgave you. And over all of those good things put on love. Love holds them all together perfectly as if they were one.

Don't lie to each other.

Let the peace that Christ gives rule in your hearts. As parts of one body, you were appointed to live in peace. And be thankful. Let Christ's word live in you like a rich treasure. Teach and correct each other wisely. Sing psalms, hymns and spiritual songs. Sing with thanks in your hearts to God. Do everything you say or do in the name of the Lord Jesus. Always give thanks to God the Father through Christ.

OK...

So Bob was right. Not even the coveted Bumblyburg Lawn and Garden trophy is worth spreading a rumor about my neighbor, Mrs. Stephenson. Even if she really has poison ivy in her garden, the judges aren't going to hear it from me. They'll probably figure that out for themselves.

God doesn't want us to say mean or bad things about each other. God wants us to spread only nice words.

Remember...
God made you special and he loves you very much!

More Favorites from Big Idea Books!

0-310-70466-9

0-310-70623-8

0-310-70540-1

0-310-70539-8

0-310-70538-X

0-310-70541-X

0-310-70784-6

0-310-70783-8

0-310-70781-1

0-310-70467-7

0-310-70702-1